L. FRANK BAUM'S

The Wizard of Oz

THE GRAPHIC NOVEL

ADAPTED BY

MICHAEL CAVALLARO

Visit us at www.abdopub.com

Spotlight, a division of ABDO Publishing Company, is a distributor of high quality reinforced library bound editions for schools and libraries.

This library bound edition is published by arrangement with Penguin Young Readers Group, a member of Penguin Group (USA) Inc.

Library of Congress Cataloging-In-Publication Data

PUFFIN BOOKS
Published by the Penguin Group
Penguin Young Readers Group,
345 Hudson Street, New York, NY 10014 U.S.A.

The Wizard of Oz Graphic Novel first published by Puffin Books, a division of Penguin Young Readers Group, 2005

Copyright © Byron Preiss Visual Publications, 2005
All rights reserved

A Byron Preiss Book
Byron Preiss Visual Publications
24 West 25th Street, New York, NY 10010

Adapted by Michael Cavallaro
Cover art by Michael Cavallaro
Series Editor: Dwight Jon Zimmerman
Series Assistant Editor: April Isaacs
Interior design by Raul Carvajal and Gilda Hannah
Cover design by Raul Carvajal

Puffin Books ISBN 0-14-240471-3
ISBN: 1-59961-120-1 Reinforced Library Bound Edition

All Spotlight books are reinforced library binding and manufactured in the United States of America.

L. FRANK BAUM'S

The Wizard of Oz

In our Solar System...

...on Earth...

...in America...

...in the midst of the great prairies...

...is a place called **Kansas**.

That's where **Dorothy** lived with her **Uncle Henry** and **Aunt Em**.

When Dorothy, who was an orphan, first came to her, Aunt Em had been startled by the child's laughter.

She still looked at the girl with wonder that she could find anything to laugh at.

It was **Toto** that made Dorothy laugh, and saved her from growing as gray as her surroundings.

Uncle Henry never laughed.

He worked hard from morning to night and did not know what joy was.

13

15

BUT WHERE *IS* THIS *CITY?*

IT IS EXACTLY IN THE *CENTER* OF THE COUNTRY, AND IS RULED BY *OZ*, THE *GREAT* AND *GOOD WIZARD!*

IT IS A *LONG JOURNEY, DOROTHY*, AND YOU MUST *WALK* THROUGH A COUNTRY THAT IS SOME-TIMES *PLEASANT* AND SOMETIMES *DARK* AND *TERRIBLE!*

I *CANNOT* GO *WITH YOU*. HOWEVER, I WILL USE *ALL THE MAGIC ARTS* I KNOW TO KEEP YOU FROM HARM!

THERE IS *ONE THING* I CAN GIVE YOU -- A *MARK* BY WHICH ALL WILL KNOW YOU ARE UNDER MY *PROTECTION.*

NO ONE WILL *DARE* INJURE A PERSON WHO BEARS THIS MARK--

--THE *KISS* OF THE *WITCH* OF THE *NORTH!*

20

Soon, Dorothy was walking briskly toward the *Emerald City*.

Along the way people bowed to her, for she had been the means of destroying the Wicked Witch.

Dorothy was greeted kindly and invited to supper...

...and given a room to rest in.

23

In the morning, after a hearty breakfast, she started out again along the *yellow brick road*.

She walked for several miles as the morning passed away and the sun rose higher in the clear blue sky.

I THINK IT'S ABOUT TIME WE HAD A REST, *TOTO*...

... AND *THIS* SEEMS LIKE AS GOOD A PLACE AS *ANY*...

GOOD DAY!

26

As they walked, Dorothy told the Scarecrow all about Kansas, and how *gray* everything was there, and how the cyclone had carried her to *Oz*.

OZ MAY BE *BEAUTIFUL*, BUT THERE'S *NO PLACE LIKE HOME!*

OF COURSE, THAT MAKES SENSE...

I CAN'T UNDERSTAND WHY YOU'D WISH TO LEAVE THIS *BEAUTIFUL COUNTRY* AND GO BACK TO THE DRY, GRAY PLACE YOU CALL *KANSAS*.

IF YOUR PEOPLE'S HEADS WERE *STUFFED* WITH *STRAW* LIKE MINE, YOU'D PROBABLY ALL LIVE IN THE *BEAUTIFUL PLACES*, AND THEN *KANSAS* WOULD HAVE NO PEOPLE AT ALL. IT'S FORTUNATE FOR KANSAS THAT YOU HAVE *BRAINS*.

Towards evening they came to a *great forest*, where the trees grew so *big* and *close together* that their branches met over the yellow brick road.

29

And soon...

I MIGHT HAVE STOOD THERE *ALWAYS* IF YOU HADN'T COME ALONG! YOU'VE CERTAINLY *SAVED MY LIFE!*

HOW DID YOU HAPPEN TO *BE* HERE?

WE'RE ON OUR WAY TO THE *EMERALD CITY*, TO SEE THE *GREAT OZ*. I WANT HIM TO SEND ME BACK TO KANSAS, AND THE *SCARECROW* WANTS HIM TO PUT A FEW *BRAINS* INTO HIS HEAD!

DO YOU SUPPOSE *OZ* COULD GIVE ME A *HEART*?

WELL, I *GUESS* SO.

IT WOULD BE AS *EASY* AS GIVING THE SCARECROW *BRAINS*.

TRUE. SO IF YOU WILL ALLOW ME TO JOIN YOUR PARTY, I WILL *ALSO* GO TO THE *EMERALD CITY* AND ASK *OZ* TO HELP ME!

COME ALONG! BUT YOU *MUST* TELL US HOW YOU CAME TO BE *STUCK* BACK THERE LIKE THAT!

33

I KNOW NOW THAT MY *GREATEST LOSS* WAS THE LOSS OF MY *HEART*, AND SO I'M RESOLVED TO ASK *OZ* TO GIVE ME ONE.

ALL THE SAME, I'LL ASK FOR *BRAINS* INSTEAD OF A *HEART*; FOR A *FOOL* WOULD NOT KNOW WHAT TO DO WITH A HEART IF HE *HAD* ONE!

I'LL TAKE THE *HEART*. FOR BRAINS DON'T MAKE ONE HAPPY, AND *HAPPINESS* IS THE BEST THING OF ALL.

Dorothy was puzzled, and did not say anything. She decided if she could only get back to Kansas and Aunt Em, it wouldn't matter so much whether the Woodman had no brains and the Scarecrow no heart, or each got what they wanted.

WHAT THE—

RRROOARR!!

THE LION IS THOUGHT TO BE *KING OF THE BEASTS*, AND WHILE I CAN ROAR VERY LOUDLY, AND FRIGHTEN EVERY LIVING THING, THE *TRUTH* IS THAT I SIMPLY HAVE *NO COURAGE.*

WELL, I'M GOING TO THE GREAT *OZ* TO ASK HIM FOR SOME *BRAINS.*

AND *I'M* GOING TO ASK HIM FOR A *HEART.*

AND *I'M* GOING TO ASK HIM TO SEND *TOTO* AND ME BACK TO *KANSAS.*

DO YOU THINK *OZ* COULD GIVE ME *COURAGE?*

JUST AS EASY AS HE COULD GIVE ME *BRAINS.*

OR GIVE ME A *HEART.*

OR SEND ME BACK TO *KANSAS.*

THEN, IF YOU DON'T *MIND,* I'LL GO WITH YOU, FOR MY LIFE IS SIMPLY *UNBEARABLE* WITHOUT A BIT OF *COURAGE.*

AND YOU WILL BE *VERY* WELCOME!

As they walked, the Tin Woodman stepped upon a beetle and *killed* the poor little thing.

This made him *very* unhappy, for he was always careful never to hurt any living creature.

He wept tears of *sorrow* and *regret*.

And Dorothy had to oil his joints where the tears had rusted them together again.

THIS WILL SERVE ME A *LESSON*, TO LOOK WHERE I STEP.

YOU PEOPLE WITH *HEARTS* HAVE SOMETHING TO *GUIDE* YOU, AND NEED NEVER DO WRONG. BUT I HAVE NO HEART, AND SO I MUST BE VERY CAREFUL.

WHEN *OZ* GIVES ME A *HEART* OF COURSE, I NEEDN'T MIND SO MUCH.

They spent the night under a large tree, with a great fire to warm them.

In the morning, they began to hear strange *noises*, and the Lion whispered that they were nearing the area where *Kalidahs* lived.

THEY'RE *MONSTROUS* BEASTS WITH BODIES LIKE *BEARS* AND HEADS LIKE *TIGERS*,

THEIR *CLAWS* ARE SO LONG AND SHARP, THEY COULD TEAR ME IN TWO AS EASILY AS *I* COULD KILL *TOTO*.

I'M *TERRIBLY AFRAID* OF THE *KALIDAHS*...

I'M NOT SURPRISED THAT YOU *ARE*. THEY MUST BE *DREADFUL* BEASTS!

The snarling brutes were both *dashed to pieces* on the sharp rocks at the bottom of the gulf!

WELL... I SEE WE ARE GOING TO LIVE A LITTLE WHILE *LONGER*, AND I'M GLAD OF IT, FOR IT MUST BE A VERY *UNCOMFORTABLE* THING NOT TO BE *ALIVE*.

THOSE CREATURES *FRIGHTENED* ME SO BADLY THAT MY *HEART* IS BEATING YET!

AH, I *WISH* I HAD A *HEART* TO *BEAT*...

The trees became thinner as they advanced, and in the afternoon they suddenly came upon a **broad river**, flowing swiftly just before them.

HOW SHALL WE CROSS THE RIVER?

THAT'S *EASILY* DONE...

THE *TIN WOODMAN* MUST BUILD US A *RAFT*, SO WE CAN FLOAT TO THE OTHER SIDE.

But it takes time to build a raft, so they found a cozy place under the trees where they slept until morning, while the *untiring* Woodman labored on through the night.

Early the next day, they launched their raft out across the river...

They got along quite well at first, but when they reached the middle of the river...

...the swift current swept the raft downstream, away from the road of yellow brick...

...and the water grew so deep that the long poles would not touch the bottom.

THIS IS *BAD!* IF WE CANNOT GET TO SHORE, WE'LL BE CARRIED INTO THE COUNTRY OF THE WICKED *WITCH OF THE WEST,* AND SHE WILL ENCHANT US AND MAKE US HER *SLAVES!*

NEVER! WE *MUST* GET TO THE *EMERALD CITY!*

46

47

THAT'S ALL RIGHT. I ALWAYS LIKE TO HELP ANYONE IN TROUBLE.

BUT I MUST GO NOW, FOR MY *BABIES* ARE WAITING IN THE NEST FOR ME.

I HOPE YOU FIND THE *EMERALD CITY* AND THE *GREAT OZ!*

Reunited once again, the companions set out along the river bank towards the road of yellow brick that would bring them to the *Emerald City*.

Soon...

LOOK!

51

By the time the *thousands* of field mice had assembled, each with a small piece of string, the *Tin Woodman* had constructed a cart onto which they rolled the Lion.

The tiny bits of string were fastened together to form *long ropes*, and the tiny mice, together in the *thousands*, *pulled as one!*

It all happened according to the Scarecrow's plan. And so it was that the *Cowardly Lion* was saved from the *deadly poppy field!*

It was around this time that Dorothy woke from her long sleep. She was *astonished* to find herself lying upon the grass with *thousands* of mice around her!

THANKS, YOUR HIGHNESS!

GOODBYE!

And so, they sat down by the Lion until he should awaken.

IF EVER YOU NEED US AGAIN, CALL, AND WE SHALL COME TO YOUR ASSISTANCE!

CREAK!

HALT!

WHAT DO YOU WISH IN THE EMERALD CITY?

SPEAK! WHAT BUSINESS DO YOU HAVE HERE?

OH!

I'M DOROTHY GALE, AND THESE ARE MY *FRIENDS, LION, SCARECROW* AND THE *TIN WOODMAN,* AND WE CAME HERE TO SEE THE GREAT *OZ!*

THE GREAT---!

IT'S BEEN *MANY YEARS* SINCE ANYONE'S ASKED TO SEE THE *GREAT OZ!*

YOU CAN'T GO LIKE *THAT!* THE *BRIGHTNESS* AND *GLORY* OF THE EMERALD CITY WOULD *BLIND* YOU!

YOU MUST EACH PUT ON THESE *SPECTACLES,* EVEN AS *I* WEAR, AND THEY MUST *REMAIN* ON *DAY* AND *NIGHT* WHILE YOU'RE IN THE CITY!

Dorothy and her friends were *dazzled* by the brilliance of the wonderful City. The Guardian of the Gates led them through the streets until they came to a big building in the middle of the City.

HERE ARE *STRANGERS*, AND THEY *DEMAND* TO SEE THE *GREAT OZ!*

PLEASE MAKE YOURSELVES COMFORTABLE WHILE I GO TO THE DOOR OF THE THRONE ROOM AND TELL *OZ* YOU ARE HERE!

...They waited a *long time*...

...a *really* long time...

Then finally—

I BRING NEWS!

HE WILL GRANT YOU AN AUDIENCE...

...BUT YOU MUST EACH SEE HIM *ALONE*, AND HE WILL ADMIT BUT *ONE* EACH DAY...

Guides came to show each of them to their rooms, where they could wait to see the Great Oz.

The Woodman had sharpened his axe and oiled all his joints properly.

The Scarecrow stuffed himself with fresh straw...

WINKIE COUNTRY

Castle of the Wicked Witch of the West

Emerald City

...and then the friends set out together again. This time there was no road of yellow brick to follow, so they simply headed towards the country of the *Winkies*, who were the *slaves* of the *Wicked Witch*.

As they walked, the words of the *Guardian of the Gates* came back to Dorothy...

TAKE CARE, FOR THE *WITCH* IS *WICKED* AND *FIERCE!* WHEN SHE KNOWS YOU ARE IN THE COUNTRY OF THE *WINKIES* SHE WILL FIND *YOU*, AND MAKE YOU ALL HER *SLAVES!*

...for her *eye* was as good as any *telescope*. She was *not happy* to find them in her land.

And he was *right*. Far off in her castle, the *Wicked Witch* had *already seen them* ...

With a *chattering* and *noise*, the Winged Monkeys flew away after Dorothy and her friends.

Soon...

WE HAVE OBEYED YOU AS FAR AS WE WERE ABLE. THE LION IS TIED UP IN YOUR YARD, THE OTHERS, WE DESTROYED...

BUT THE GIRL WE DARE NOT HARM, NOR THE DOG SHE CARRIES IN HER ARMS!

YOUR POWER OVER OUR BAND IS NOW ENDED!

AND YOU WILL NEVER SEE US AGAIN!!

The Witch was surprised and worried by the mark on Dorothy's forehead.

She knew well that she dare not hurt the girl in any way.

Dorothy's Silver Shoes made her tremble with fear, for she knew a powerful charm belonged to them.

The Witch was tempted to run away...

... but then she happened to look into Dorothy's *eyes*, and saw how *simple* the soul behind them was.

She saw that the girl did not know of the power the Silver Shoes gave her, and all fear left the Witch.

COME WITH ME...

...AND SEE THAT YOU MIND *EVERYTHING* I TELL YOU, OR ELSE I'LL MAKE AN *END* OF YOU AS I DID OF YOUR *FRIENDS!*

What the Witch *didn't* know, was that every night while she was asleep, Dorothy would sneak out with some food from the cupboard.

The Cowardly Lion had *plenty* to eat.

They would talk of their troubles and try to plan a way to *escape*. Sometimes Dorothy cried bitterly, for she feared she'd never get back to Kansas and Aunt Em again.

Then, every day their troubles started anew. The Witch would come to the gate and ask:

ARE YOU READY TO BE *HARNESSED* LIKE A HORSE?

NEVER!

AND IF YOU COME NEAR ME I'LL BITE YOU!!

SUIT YOURSELF! AT THIS RATE, YOU'LL SOON *STARVE* TO *DEATH*, YOU SILLY BEAST!

Now the Wicked Witch had a great longing to have for her own the **Silver Shoes** which Dorothy always wore.

Her **Bees** and her **Crows** and her **Wolves** were lying in heaps, and she had used up all the power of the **Golden Cap**.

If she could only get hold of the **Silver Shoes**, they would give her more power than all the other things she had lost.

The Wicked Witch decided she would watch Dorothy carefully, and wait for an opportunity to **steal** the shoes...

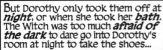

But Dorothy only took them off at **night**, or when she took her **bath**. The Witch was too much **afraid of the dark** to dare go into Dorothy's room at night to take the shoes...

...and her dread of **water** was even greater than her fear of the dark, so she **never** came near when Dorothy was bathing.

Indeed, the old Witch **never touched water**, nor ever let water **touch her** in any way.

89

And that was indeed the end of the **Wicked Witch of the West.**

Together, they went once more into the castle.

WE'D BE *DELIGHTED* TO HELP YOU FIND YOUR FRIENDS.

They travelled until they came to the rocky plain where the Winged Monkeys had left their friends.

They gathered up all the scattered pieces of the Scarecrow's clothes...

...and all the battered and bent parts of the Tin Woodman, and carried them back to the castle.

The Winkies that were good with needle and thread stitched the Scarecrow's clothes back together and stuffed him again with nice, clean straw.

Meanwhile, the *tinsmiths* set themselves to the difficult task of repairing all the damage that had been done to the poor Tin Woodman.

For three days and four nights they hammered, twisted, bent, soldered, polished and pounded at the legs and body and head of the Tin Woodman while Dorothy and the others waited...

...and *waited*...

...until *finally*...

But a long time later...

...um...

THAT *ROCK* LOOKS *VERY FAMILIAR.*

we're going around in circles.

hm.

YES, WE'VE SURELY LOST OUR WAY, AND UNLESS WE *FIND IT* AGAIN IN TIME TO REACH THE *EMERALD CITY*, I SHALL *NEVER* GET MY BRAINS.

NOR I MY HEART.

I HAVEN'T THE *COURAGE* TO KEEP *TRAMPING FOREVER*, WITHOUT GETTING *ANYWHERE* AT ALL.

SUPPOSE WE CALL THE *FIELD MICE!* THEY COULD PROBABLY TELL US THE WAY TO THE EMERALD CITY!

MANY YEARS AGO, WE WERE A *FREE PEOPLE*, LIVING HAPPILY IN THE GREAT FOREST THAT GREW NEAR THE CASTLE OF THE PRINCESS *GAYELETTE*, WHO WAS ALSO A *POWERFUL SORCERESS*.

AT THAT TIME, *MY GRANDFATHER* WAS *KING* OF THE *WINGED MONKEYS*. ONE DAY, THEY SAW A MAN WALKING BESIDE THE RIVER, AND THEY DECIDED TO PLAY A PRANK ON HIM. THEY SNATCHED HIM UP AND *DROPPED* HIM IN THE RIVER!

THE MAN WAS A *GOOD SPORT* AND HE LAUGHED AT THE JOKE AS HE DUMPED THE WATER FROM HIS *GOLDEN CAP*, BUT THEN OUT RAN *GAYELETTE*.

THE MAN TURNED OUT TO BE *QUELALA*, WHO WAS SOON TO *MARRY* GAYELETTE, AND THE *GOLDEN CAP* WAS HER *GIFT* TO HIM. THE SORCERESS WAS *FURIOUS* AT HIS TREATMENT, AND WANTED TO TIE UP ALL THE MONKEYS AND THROW THEM IN THE RIVER, BUT QUELALA TOOK *PITY* ON THEM AND SPOKE KINDLY IN THEIR DEFENSE.

GAYELETTE SPARED THEM, ON CONDITION THAT THE WINGED MONKEYS SHOULD EVER AFTER DO *THREE TIMES* THE BIDDING OF THE OWNER OF THE CAP.

QUELALA WAS THE *FIRST* OWNER OF THE CAP, AND HIS ONLY WISH WAS THAT WE KEEP TO WHERE HIS BRIDE COULD NEVER AGAIN SEE US, WHICH WE WERE GLAD TO DO.

THAT WAS ALL WE EVER HAD TO DO UNTIL THE GOLDEN CAP FELL INTO THE HANDS OF THE *WICKED WITCH OF THE WEST*, WHO MADE US *ENSLAVE THE WINKIES...*

THEN, SHE ORDERED US TO DRIVE *OZ* HIMSELF OUT OF THE LAND OF THE WEST. FINALLY, WE WERE MADE TO CAPTURE *YOU,* AND THAT *RELEASED* US FROM THE WITCH'S SERVICE.

NOW THE *GOLDEN CAP* IS *YOURS,* AND *THREE TIMES* YOU HAVE THE RIGHT TO LAY YOUR WISHES UPON US!

They passed through the gate into the *Emerald City*, and as they went the Guardian announced to the astonished people that the *Wicked Witch of the West* had been *destroyed*.

MAKE WAY!

THE STRANGERS HAVE DEFEATED THE WICKED WITCH OF THE WEST!

The soldier with the green whiskers was still on guard before the door, but he let them in at once.

SHOW THEM TO THEIR OLD ROOMS *AT ONCE*, SO THEY MAY REST UNTIL THE *GREAT OZ* IS READY TO RECEIVE THEM!

They thought the Great Wizard would send for them at once...

...but they had no word from him the next day...

...nor the next...

...nor the next.

At last, they grew vexed that Oz would treat them in so poor a fashion.

WE'VE HAD ABOUT *ENOUGH* OF THIS *WAITING!* *PLEASE* TAKE THIS MESSAGE TO *OZ* RIGHT AWAY!

And so he did.

"...AND SO, IF YOU DO NOT SEE US *AT ONCE*, WE SHALL CALL THE *WINGED MONKEYS* TO HELP US FIND OUT IF YOU KEEP YOUR PROMISES OR NOT!"

The Wizard did not wish to meet the Winged Monkeys again. He sent word for Dorothy and her friends to come to him at four minutes after nine o'clock the next morning.

113

WHO ARE YOU?

I AM OZ, THE GREAT AND TERRIBLE!

er...BUT DON'T STRIKE ME --*PLEASE DON'T!*-- AND I'LL DO ANYTHING YOU WANT ME TO...

I THOUGHT *OZ* WAS A GREAT *HEAD.*

I THOUGHT *OZ* WAS A *LOVELY LADY.*

AND *I* THOUGHT *OZ* WAS A *TERRIBLE BEAST.*

I THOUGHT *OZ* WAS A *BALL* OF *FIRE.*

NO...

...YOU'RE ALL *WRONG.*

I'VE BEEN *MAKING BELIEVE.*

"MAKING BELIEVE"? ARE YOU NOT A *GREAT WIZARD?*

HUSH, MY DEAR!

DON'T SPEAK SO *LOUDLY,* OR I'LL BE *RUINED!*

But...

...aren't you?

Not a *bit,* my dear.

I'm just a *common man.*

YOU'RE *MORE* THAN *THAT*-- --YOU'RE A *HUMBUG!*

EXACTLY SO. THOUGH NO ONE KNOWS IT BUT YOU FOUR AND MYSELF. I'VE FOOLED EVERYONE SO LONG THAT I THOUGHT I'D *NEVER* BE FOUND OUT.

I DON'T *UNDERSTAND.* HOW DID YOU APPEAR AS ALL THOSE *CREATURES?*

IT WAS ALL *TRICKERY,* MY DEAR; HIDDEN ROPES, MASKS, *ILLUSION* AND *VENTRILOQUISM!*

I'VE BECOME QUITE A *MASTER* OF IT ALL. BUT, ALAS, IT'S NOT TRUE *MAGIC.*

PLEASE, SIT DOWN, AND I'LL TELL YOU MY STORY, SO THAT YOU WON'T *JUDGE* ME TOO HARSHLY!

I WAS BORN IN *OMAHA,* AND AS A YOUNG MAN, I BECAME A *BALLOONIST* FOR THE CIRCUS!

ONE DAY, I WENT UP IN MY BALLOON, AND THE *ROPES* BECAME *TWISTED...*

A CURRENT OF AIR STRUCK MY CRAFT AND CARRIED IT MANY, MANY MILES!

BUT, *ISN'T* EVERYTHING HERE *GREEN*?

NO MORE THAN IN ANY *OTHER* CITY.

MY PEOPLE HAVE WORN *GREEN GLASSES* SO LONG THAT MOST OF THEM THINK IT REALLY *IS* AN *EMERALD CITY*.

MY GREATEST FEAR, OTHER THAN BEING *FOUND OUT*, HAS BEEN THE *WITCHES*...

WHILE *I* HAD NO MAGICAL POWERS, *THEY* WERE REALLY ABLE TO DO MANY WONDERFUL THINGS.

THE WITCHES OF THE *EAST* AND *WEST* WERE TERRIBLY *WICKED*...

...HAD THEY NOT THOUGHT ME MORE POWERFUL THAN THEMSELVES, THEY WOULD SURELY HAVE *DESTROYED* ME.

I WAS SO PLEASED WHEN I HEARD YOUR *HOUSE* HAD FALLEN ON THE *WICKED WITCH OF THE EAST*. I WAS WILLING TO PROMISE *ANYTHING* IF YOU'D ONLY DO AWAY WITH THE *OTHER* WITCH...

...BUT NOW I'M ASHAMED TO SAY THAT I CAN'T KEEP MY PROMISES.

I THINK YOU'RE A *VERY BAD MAN*.

OH, *DEAR ME, NO!*

I'M A *VERY GOOD MAN*...

...I'M JUST A *VERY BAD* WIZARD.

118

WE SHALL HAVE TO THINK ABOUT THAT, MY DEAR.

GIVE ME TWO OR THREE DAYS TO CONSIDER THE MATTER AND I'LL TRY TO FIND A WAY TO CARRY YOU OVER THE *DESERT.*

IN THE MEANTIME, YOU ARE MY *GUESTS* HERE IN THE PALACE.

I ONLY ASK THAT YOU KEEP MY SECRET AND TELL NO ONE THAT I'M A *HUMBUG.*

They agreed to say nothing of what they had learned, and went back to their rooms.

For three days Dorothy heard nothing from Oz. These were sad days for her, although her friends were all quite happy and contented.

Then...

DOROTHY! I THINK I'VE FOUND THE WAY TO GET YOU OUT OF THIS COUNTRY!

AND BACK TO KANSAS?

BUT HOW?

YOU SEE, WHEN I CAME HERE IT WAS IN A BALLOON. YOU WERE CARRIED BY A CYCLONE. SO--

WELL, THE FIRST THING TO DO IS TO CROSS THE DESERT!

--THE BEST WAY TO GET ACROSS THE DESERT IS THROUGH THE AIR! I'VE BEEN THINKING THE MATTER OVER, AND I BELIEVE THAT, TOGETHER, WE CAN MAKE A BALLOON AND FLOAT OVER THE DESERT!

"WE"? ARE YOU GOING WITH ME?

YES, OF COURSE! I'M TIRED OF BEING SUCH A HUMBUG! I'D MUCH RATHER GO BACK TO KANSAS AND BE IN A CIRCUS AGAIN. WHAT DO YOU SAY? SHALL WE TRY?

YES WE SHALL! I'LL BE GLAD TO HAVE YOUR COMPANY!

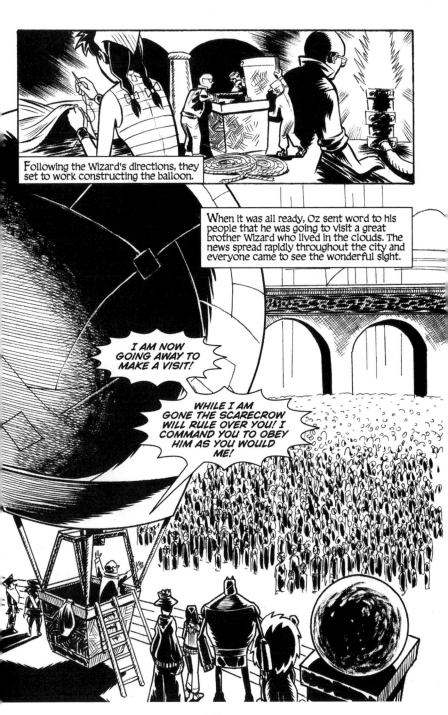

Following the Wizard's directions, they set to work constructing the balloon.

When it was all ready, Oz sent word to his people that he was going to visit a great brother Wizard who lived in the clouds. The news spread rapidly throughout the city and everyone came to see the wonderful sight.

I AM NOW GOING AWAY TO MAKE A VISIT!

WHILE I AM GONE THE SCARECROW WILL RULE OVER YOU! I COMMAND YOU TO OBEY HIM AS YOU WOULD ME!

For days, though, Dorothy would not be comforted.

Her friends thought and thought for a way to get her back to Kansas.

I'VE *GOT IT!* YOU CAN ASK THE *WINGED MONKEYS* TO FLY YOU HOME!

So Dorothy called the Monkeys, but...

THAT CANNOT BE DONE!

WE BELONG TO THIS COUNTRY ALONE, AND CANNOT LEAVE IT!

AND *NOW* I'VE *WASTED* A WISH!

Finally, a few days later...

IF *ANYONE* CAN HELP, IT'S *GLINDA*, THE *GOOD WITCH OF THE SOUTH!*

THEN WE SHALL GO TOMORROW MORNING!

LET US ALL GET READY, FOR IT WILL BE A LONG JOURNEY!

COME QUICKLY!

I BELIEVE THE WAY IS *CLEAR* NOW!

The four travellers walked with ease through the trees, which from that point did *nothing* to keep them back.

Then, after a long and tiresome walk through the underbrush, they came to an opening in the wood...

IT LOOKS LIKE THE ANIMALS ARE HOLDING A *MEETING...*

WHAT IS YOUR *TROUBLE?*

WE ARE ALL *THREATENED* BY A FIERCE ENEMY THAT HAS COME TO THIS FOREST!

IT IS A *TREMENDOUS MONSTER* THAT SEIZES AND *EATS* ANIMALS! NONE OF US ARE SAFE WHILE IT'S ALIVE! WE CALLED A MEETING TO DECIDE HOW TO PROTECT OURSELVES.

IF I PUT AN END TO YOUR ENEMY, WILL YOU *BOW DOWN* TO ME AND *OBEY* ME AS *KING OF THE FOREST?*

WE WILL DO THAT *GLADLY!*

THEN I WILL *GO* AT ONCE TO FIGHT THIS MONSTER!

TAKE GOOD CARE OF THESE *FRIENDS* OF MINE!

I'M BACK!

YOU NEED FEAR YOUR ENEMY *NO LONGER!*

YOUR HIGHNESS!

I PROMISE TO RETURN AND RULE HERE ONCE *DOROTHY* IS ON HER WAY HOME!

The animals were grateful at having been saved from the monster, and the four travellers passed through the rest of the forest without trouble.

WELCOME, FRIENDS!

DOROTHY, WHAT CAN I DO FOR YOU, MY CHILD?

Glinda was both beautiful and young to their eyes. Her hair was a rich red, her dress was pure white, and her blue eyes looked kindly upon Dorothy.

Dorothy told the witch all her story...

...MY GREATEST WISH NOW IS TO GET BACK TO *KANSAS*...

BLESS YOUR HEART! I'M SURE I CAN HELP YOU...

...BUT IF I DO, YOU MUST GIVE ME THE *GOLDEN CAP!*

TIN WOODMAN, WHAT WILL BECOME OF YOU WHEN DOROTHY LEAVES THIS COUNTRY?

THE WINKIES WERE VERY *KIND* TO ME, AND ASKED ME TO *RULE OVER THEM* AFTER THE *WICKED WITCH* DIED. I SHOULD VERY MUCH LIKE TO *RETURN* TO THEIR COUNTRY IN THE WEST.

MY SECOND COMMAND TO THE WINGED MONKEYS WILL BE TO CARRY YOU SAFELY TO THE LAND OF THE WINKIES!

I'M SURE YOU'LL RULE OVER THEM *WISELY* AND *WELL!*

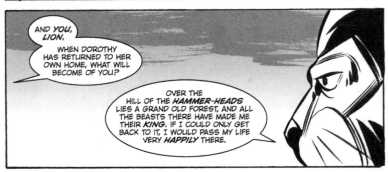

AND *YOU, LION,* WHEN DOROTHY HAS RETURNED TO HER OWN HOME, WHAT WILL BECOME OF YOU?

OVER THE HILL OF THE *HAMMER-HEADS* LIES A GRAND OLD FOREST, AND ALL THE BEASTS THERE HAVE MADE ME THEIR *KING.* IF I COULD ONLY GET BACK TO IT, I WOULD PASS MY LIFE VERY *HAPPILY* THERE.

MY THIRD COMMAND TO THE WINGED MONKEYS WILL BE TO CARRY YOU TO YOUR FOREST!

THEN, HAVING USED UP THE POWERS OF THE *GOLDEN CAP,* I SHALL GIVE IT TO THE *KING* OF THE *MONKEYS,* THAT HE AND HIS BAND MAY BE *FREE* FOR *EVERMORE.*

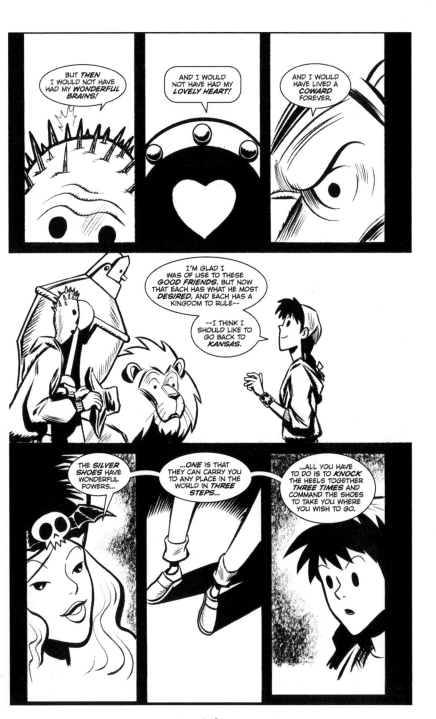

144

145

146

Just before her was the new house Uncle Henry had built after the cyclone had carried the old one away.

The Silver Shoes had fallen off during the flight through the air.

But Dorothy no longer cared...

YAP! YAP!

147